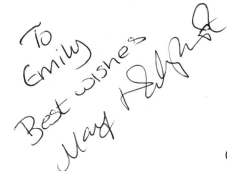

To
Emily
Best wishes
May Halyburton

D0524924

First published in Great Britain by
WhiteWater Publishing Ltd

ISBN 978-1-909797-38-3

CD Full Tracklist

1. Bessy's Theme (Fairy Dance)
2. London Bridge
3. Skye Boat Song
4. Frère Jacques
5. A Round with Friends (Frère Jacques)
6. Principal Bass' Solo
7. Principal Bass and Bessy's Duet
8. Rakes of Mallow
9. Bessy's Bolero
10. Marching with Carmen
11. My Love She's but a Lassie Yet
12. Sweet Dreams
13. Bessy does Baroque
14. Fairy Dance Finale

The following tracks are the accompaniments alone. Why not pretend to be Bessy and sing-along with Petra? If you would like to try playing these melodies on your instrument, then go to **www.bessybass.com/shop** where you can purchase the music book which has the pieces in bass, treble and alto clef forms.

15. Bessy's Theme (Fairy Dance) - Accompaniment
16. London Bridge - Accompaniment
17. Skye Boat Song - Accompaniment
18. Frère Jacques - Accompaniment
19. A Round with Friends (Frère Jacques) - Accompaniment
20. Principal Bass and Bessy's Duet - Accompaniment
21. Rakes of Mallow - Accompaniment
22. Bessy's Bolero - Accompaniment
23. Marching with Carmen - Accompaniment
24. My Love She's but a Lassie Yet - Accompaniment
25. Sweet Dreams - Accompaniment
26. Bessy does Baroque - Accompaniment
27. Fairy Dance Finale - Accompaniment

Introduction

The character Bessy Bass came to be when my teacher at the Royal Scottish Academy of Music and Drama (now the Royal Conservatoire of Scotland) set me the assignment of creating a demonstration performance to introduce the double bass to children. I decided to create a story and accompany it with music in order to show off the capabilities and versatility of the instrument. After trying this out at a junior branch of a local music club and encouraged by the reaction of my young audience, I decided to develop the story further and in 2005, I wrote the first draft of Around The World With Bessy – part 1 – Europe, the first in a series of stories accompanied by music for children. However, due to my busy work schedule as a freelance double bassist and teacher and unsure of how to take the next step with Bessy, I carefully filed her away. Nine years later I found the inspiration and courage to revisit this story, and together with encouragement from several friends, I rescued her from the shelf, edited parts of the story and called pianist and composer Lynda Cochrane!

I was introduced to Mary Thomson at WhiteWater Publishing who enthusiastically found ways of preparing Bessy to appeal to a whole primary school in the form of a wonderful story book for the older children and a beautiful picture book for the younger ones. Mary then introduced me to her very talented daughter, Robyn, who has skilfully brought Bessy to life with her beautiful illustrations. Robyn, who is still at school, already has an impressive portfolio of art work and despite suffering from dyslexia, writes and illustrates her own stories. Bessy is her first professional contract and I am sure is the first step of her own very successful career.

The project is set on many levels. At the very least, I aim to promote reading amongst children and take them on a fantastical journey, helping to develop their imagination, but as they begin to explore the diverse world of music, subconsciously it may be their first step to finding an instrument of their own to learn, which will provide them with lifelong skills and enjoyment as well as an appreciation of a variety of genres of music. The stories are conducive to the Curriculum for Excellence in Scotland and could be used in primary schools as a class or even a whole school project. Bessy has her own website, where project ideas as well as other exciting features and articles can be found **(www.bessybass.com)**.

The project includes a story book, a picture book, and a music book, all with accompanying CDs, as well as an audio book narrated by John Cavanagh and a live touring show which can be recreated on several levels. Lynda has written and arranged some beautiful pieces to accompany the story. The pieces are designed not only to highlight the story but also to provide a playlist of melodies suitable for young children, performed on the double bass, as several of my young double bass students have had difficulty in finding such a recording. All the pieces can be played by children as they range from beginner to grade 4 level, so the sheet music is published separately and the young player can be accompanied by an experienced pianist, the backing track CD or a young pianist friend, as Lynda has also prepared an easy piano accompaniment for most of the pieces. The pieces are available in bass, alto and treble clef forms, so that they can be played on other instruments too.

The double bass has grown in popularity amongst children over the past 25 years or so. This is greatly due to the availability of mini basses in a variety of sizes, meaning that children can start playing at a much younger age. However, double bassists are still very much outnumbered by players of other members of the string family. This has a knock on effect to school and regional children's and youth orchestras who often have the problem of depleted double bass sections. Without a solid foundation, it makes it much harder for any ensemble or orchestra to function. With this project, I aim to create awareness of the double bass and later on in future stories, some of the other more "endangered" instruments, alongside the more popular instruments, so that children have the opportunity to appreciate and possibly learn to play them should they choose to.

As well as an introduction to music, the stories convey a message of inclusion, friendship and kindness. The double bass makes an ideal central character as it is a very versatile instrument vital to most ensembles. Its cumbersome size makes it stand out from the rest of the instruments but at the same time it is usually in the background rather than central stage.

Music is an international language and often provides the chance to travel all over the world. Playing the double bass opened up an exciting world to me over the years and I would like to use that experience to encourage children to join Bessy and explore the world with music.

Thanks To ...

Like all superstars, Bessy has quite an entourage of helpers and supporters. I have been overwhelmed by the generous help, advice and encouragement I have received from my wonderful family, friends and colleagues and would like to say a huge thank you to **all** who helped Bessy travel from my imagination to yours. In particular, I would like to thank:

Ninian Perry for setting me the original assignment.

The Team:-
Lynda Cochrane for her wonderful additions to the double bass repertoire, her beautiful piano playing on the CD and her unfaltering support as my business partner; Robyn Thomson for her exquisite illustrations bringing Bessy to life; Mary Thomson for her skill, enthusiasm and creativity in bringing Bessy to the page; John Cavanagh for his enthusiasm, eloquent narration and recording of the audio book text; Paul Baxter and Delphian Records for a fantastic recording session of the music CD and the preparation of the audio book; My partner Norman Motion for tuning the piano at the recording session and for being my rock throughout this first project; Brian Prentice for his enthusiastic support, technical advice, preparation of the music CDs for the manufacturers and recording the demo CD; Matthew Motion for building our fantastic website; BirnamCD for their help, patience and manufacture of the CDs; Gordon Mavor of Gordon Mavor & Co Accountants for his enthusiasm, support and expertise; and Susan McFadden and the team at Blackadders Solicitors who have taken such great care of all things legal.

The Support Network:-
Jane Colvin, Angela Currie, Jane Ferguson, Jane Gardner, Roddy Long and Hazel Woodcock for their long term support and encouragement over the past decade; Seonaid Aitken for her stage advice; James and Ruth Davie for their enthusiasm and generous help in preparing for Bessy's Launch; Claire Docherty and George

Watson's College for a school demonstration opportunity; Richard Ingham and Margaret Douglass for their enthusiasm, support advice and for providing the photographs and sounds of Bessy's village for the show; Richard Payne for his score preparation words of wisdom; Cerin Richardson for her advice and introducing me to Mary Thomson; Gillian O'Dempsey for her encouragement and introducing me to Cerin; James Ross for his advice and encouragement; Mike McGeary, Lynette and Bob Whitney for advice, encouragement and introducing me to BirnamCD; The team at Creative Enterprise, and in particular Jim Sutherland for his enthusiasm, encouragement and helpful advice; The Musician's Union, Duncan McCrone and the team at MCPS for their patience and advice; and Robert Lindsay who introduced me to Susan McFadden.

The very generous sponsors whose kind contributions have made an incredible difference to this project:-
Sir Richard Dunbar of Hempriggs, Bt., for his support, encouragement and generous donation; Sir Gerald and Lady Elliot for their very generous personal donation; My dear friend Alison Gregson, who not only generously contributed to the project, but also for her enthusiasm, support and tea and scone conferences; My partner, Norman Motion for his generous contribution to Bessy's Launch; The Violin Shop in Glasgow for their very generous donation and support; and the RSNO for their generous donation of the Henry Wood Hall for the CD recording.

And finally, a special thank you to the Mums:-
Lynda's mum, Liz Cochrane for her encouragement, proof reading, support and advice; and my mum, May Johnston who has proof read, advised, designed and made Bessy's wonderful scarf from Robyn's drawings, made countless cups of tea and generally helped me to keep my sanity throughout the last year.

To Ryan and Melissa,
Kieran, Natasha and Toby,
Yohann,
Martha and Joseph

And

In memory of my late father,
James A Johnston
and dear friend
Jean Ferguson.

AROUND THE WORLD

WITH
Bessy
PART ONE
EUROPE

by
MAY HALYBURTON

Chapter 1 – London Calling

It was a bright, sunny morning in the quaint, coastal village of Lower Largo in Scotland.

Bessy Bass roused from a gentle sleep to the sound of birds singing outside her window. She gave an enormous yawn and stretched, before suddenly remembering that today was the start of her **big adventure!**

"Yipee!" she exclaimed, as she jumped out of bed, dressed in her favourite scarf and ran to the kitchen to eat her breakfast.

She quickly munched a bowl of crotchets and quavers, thinking all the time about the wonderful holiday she would have.

As soon as her breakfast was cleared away, she rushed to pack the last of her things. She had to sit on her suitcase to close it!

Finally, with all her strength, Bessy managed to pull the zipper all the way around and she was ready to leave.

With a contented sigh she skipped out of the front door, locked it securely and headed off to the station.

There, on the platform, were her three best friends; Bertie Bagpipes, Fiona Fiddle and Dudley Drum.
"Oh what a lovely surprise!" cried Bessy
"We wanted to give you a proper send off!" said Fiona.

"We've made you a playlist of Scottish songs for you to take with you, so that you won't get homesick!" said Dudley as he handed Bessy his MP3 player.

"Thank you so much! This is great!" chirped Bessy. "Oh brilliant, you've started with my favourite!" And she began to sing 'Fairy Dance' which her mother had taught her when she was very young.

The others joined in as Bessy boarded the train and her friends waved from the platform.

Then, with a small lurch, the carriage began to move. Bessy and her friends carried on waving until they looked like tiny dots on the horizon. Bessy was sad to leave her friends but she knew she could listen to their songs any time she felt lonely.

As she settled into her seat, she looked out of the window and once again became excited about her trip.

Bessy passed through sleepy villages and busy towns and saw lush, green countryside and the deep, blue sea. She was having fun.

At last the train pulled into King's Cross station and Bessy prepared to get off the train. This was her first stop ... London.

"Wow!" she gasped as she headed through the city.

She saw lots of sights, including Buckingham Palace, the Tower of London and the Houses of Parliament. She also saw several bridges spanning the River Thames and was immediately reminded of the old song 'London Bridge'. She began humming the familiar melody.

Bessy made her way to the guest house where she would be staying. It was quite an adventure in itself for the young double bass, as it involved a ride on the underground, followed by a short trip on a bus!

When she finally arrived, exhausted by her exciting day, she headed to her room, ready for a good night's sleep.

Chapter 2 – Off to France

The next day, feeling completely refreshed, Bessy continued on her journey south.

She headed back to the station (this time in a taxi) where she was going to catch the Eurostar to Paris.

Bessy was a little anxious about going through the Channel Tunnel but as the train pulled away she began humming one of Bertie, Fiona and Dudley's songs and soon felt better.

Soon Bessy arrived in Paris and was met
at the station by her cousin Violette Violin.

"Bonjour Bessy!" cried Violette.

"Oooolala!" giggled Bessy. "What an amazing
place!"

Violette took Bessy on a trip round the city.
She saw the Eiffel Tower and the Arc de
Triomphe and wandered down the
Champs-Élysées.

"C'est fantastique!" she said happily.

The next day Violette took Bessy to meet some of her friends.

Bessy had learned to say "Bonjour" and "Je m'appelle Bessy." She was very pleased with herself but found it quite difficult to understand everything Violette and her friends were saying.

Violette noticed that Bessy had gone quiet and looked a little lost, so she quickly thought of a way to cheer her up.

"I know what we should do," began Violette.

"Let's teach Bessy to sing one of our songs!"

"Bonne idée!" chorused the group and they began to sing 'Frère Jacques' to Bessy.

Once Bessy had learned the song, Violette suggested they try singing it in a round.

"Oooo yes. Let's try!" agreed Bessy and the friends began to sing.

"That was great!" Bessy grinned when they finally came to an end. "We've been singing for ages! I think I'm getting a little hoarse!" she croaked.

Violette and Bessy then said "Au revoir" to the others and headed off to the big concert hall in the centre of town.

"What are we going to listen to?" asked Bessy.

Violette explained that they were going to hear a rehearsal of a big symphony by the famous Austrian composer called Gustav Mahler.

Bessy and Violette sat in the wings of the stage and listened to the wonderful music performed by the enormous symphony orchestra.

"So many instruments," whispered Bessy "What a wonderful sound!"

"C'est magnifique!" agreed Violette.

Just then, the orchestra began the slow movement of the symphony. Bessy couldn't believe her ears. The huge double bass at the front of the section, known as the principal double bass, began to sing a solo.

"Wow!" she gasped.

Violette smiled. The principal double bass was singing a melody very similar to 'Frère Jacques', only this one was in a minor key which made it sound quite sad but enchanting.

After the rehearsal had finished, Violette had arranged for Bessy to meet the principal double bass. Excitedly, Bessy ran on to the stage.

"Aah, you must be Bessy" he said gently.

"Yes," whispered Bessy suddenly quite shy.

"Did you enjoy the symphony?" asked the big double bass in his warm, deep tones.

"Oh yes!" gasped Bessy. "It was wonderful and your solo was so beautiful."

"Merci beaucoup, mademoiselle," replied the principal bass.

"Perhaps you would like to sing a duet with me?" he asked.

"Yes pleeeeease!" responded Bessy and he taught her how to sing the accompaniment to his solo, so they could sing together.

"Bravo! Bravo!" shouted Violette, wildly applauding.

Bessy and Violette said "Merci!" and "Au revoir!" to the principal bass and happily skipped off back to Violette's house.

"What a perfect day!" sighed Bessy contently as she climbed the stairs to her room. "Thank you Violette."

Violette smiled warmly and said goodnight to her cousin.

Chapter 3 – Spain here we come!

After spending a few more days with Violette, Bessy repacked her case and got ready for the next part of her journey. Violette had kindly loaned Bessy her special car, Henri.

Bessy smiled at the car and Henri smiled back. She was thrilled. Henri was a smart, shiny, yellow classic car with a roof that folded back to let the sunshine in and Bessy stretch out!

"Merci beaucoup," she cried as she eagerly climbed into the car.

"Now you will always have a good friend with you," said Violette.

"Au revoir Violette!" shouted Bessy, as she and Henri headed off in the direction of Spain, "... and thank you for everything."

"Au revoir Bessy!" Violette called as she waved the pair on their way. "Henri, I'll see you soon in Germany!"

Bessy and Henri tootled their way round the winding roads and over the hills. After a while, the travellers became a little tired and Bessy began to miss her cousin, Violette. Then she remembered her collection of songs from home. She picked one and began to sing it.

"C'est formidable!" cheered Henri who felt energised by the lively music. Bessy felt better too and smiled as the beautiful scenery went by. Very soon Bessy saw a sign which read 'Seville 15km'. "We're nearly there!" she exclaimed. "Hooray!" chorused the happy travellers.

A short while later, the pair pulled up in front of a lovely big house where Bessy's friend, Gustavo Guitar lived. Henri tooted his horn and Gustavo came running to the front gate.

"¡Hola!" greeted Gustavo enthusiastically as Bessy climbed out of the car.

"¡Hola Gustavo!" replied Bessy just as excitedly.

"Great to see you Bessy. How was your trip?

"Long but good," she sleepily replied and introduced Gustavo to Henri. Henri went into the garage for a well earned rest and Bessy followed Gustavo into the house, where she was treated to a delicious meal of Spanish omelette and lots of tasty tapas dishes.

The next morning Bessy woke up early feeling refreshed. After breakfast, Gustavo and Bessy headed into the city.

"Where are we going?" asked Bessy.

"First of all," said Gustavo, "we are going to see my friends Pepe and Pilar. They are Flamenco dancers and I am going to sing some authentic Spanish music for them to dance to."

"Brilliant!" whooped Bessy, who was absolutely thrilled. As Bessy and Gustavo entered the dance studio, they heard the very strong sound of castanets.

"Trrrum click-e-ty trrrum click-e-ty stomp stomp,
trrrum click-e-ty trrrum click-e-ty stomp stomp....."

As she watched, Bessy marvelled at the elegant steps and colourful costumes of the dancers as well as the vibrant sounds of the music that was accompanying them.

When the dancers came to a final flourish, Bessy cheered and clapped.

"That was '¡Fantastico!'" said Bessy.

"¡Gracias!" replied Pepe and Pilar, "And thank you for coming to visit us."

Bessy skipped down the road trying to imitate some of the fancy footwork she had just seen.

"You enjoyed that," laughed Gustavo.

"Oh yes Gustavo. That was wonderful!"

The two friends spent the next few days sightseeing and Bessy bought some postcards to send to Bertie Bagpipes, Fiona Fiddle and Dudley Drum in Scotland and one for Violette in Paris.

Henri had also been doing a bit of sightseeing himself and Bessy helped him to send a postcard to Violette.

On the last night of her stay in Spain, Gustavo had organised a big surprise for Bessy. She was going to see a performance of the opera 'Carmen', a Spanish story set to music by the French composer Georges Bizet.

Bessy sat spellbound throughout the entire performance. She especially enjoyed the 'March'.

"I must learn to sing that," she thought to herself.
When the curtain fell for the last time, Bessy turned to Gustavo and gave him a big hug.

"That was sooooo beautiful!" she gasped

"I thought you would enjoy it," smiled Gustavo.
The next morning Bessy and Henri prepared for the next stage of their journey.

"Thank you for such a lovely time Gustavo," said Bessy.
"It has been wonderful."

"It has," agreed Gustavo. "You two take care on your travels. I'll come visit you in Scotland soon!"

"¡Excelente!" shouted Bessy and the two travellers headed off in the direction of Italy.

Chapter 4 – Viva Italia!

It was a long journey but time passed very quickly. Henri reminded Bessy of the song she had learned from Violette and her friends and they sang it as a round over and over.

Then Bessy sang some more of her favourite songs her friends from home had given her and taught them to Henri.

The happy pair sang until they finally arrived at their next destination....Milan, Italy.

"Wow! What an amazing place!" exclaimed Bessy.

"It certainly is!" gasped Henri, as he tried to steer Bessy out of the rush hour traffic into the quiet street where her Great Uncle Bernardo lived.

Great Uncle Bernardo, or Prozio Bernardo as Bessy called him, was a very distinguished five-string double bass who had spent most of his working life at the famous opera house, Teatro alla Scala. He had performed with all the famous opera singers and was well respected by all his former colleagues. Prozio Bernardo was now officially retired but spent much of his time teaching young double basses who were keen to follow in his footsteps.

Bessy was very excited about seeing her great uncle.

She had only met him once before when she was very young.

As Bessy and Henri drove up the driveway, the big, heavy front door opened slowly and Prozio Bernardo came out onto the doorstep.

"Buonasera Bessy!" he bellowed in his rich, deep voice.

"Buonasera Prozio Bernardo!" replied Bessy.

Prozio Bernardo helped Bessy into the house with her suitcase and opened the garage door for Henri, who was ready for a big, long sleep.

Bessy was also very tired, so after a beautiful meal of pasta and garlic bread, she headed up the stairs to her room and immediately fell asleep.

And sleep she did!

It was nearly 11 o'clock when Bessy awoke the next morning. She had been dreaming about being a world famous soloist and was singing a beautiful melody, centre stage in a very prestigious concert hall. She was singing so beautifully. She had the rich tone she had been working so hard to achieve and the audience were spellbound by her performance.

As she slowly opened her eyes, the vision of her standing proudly, with the magnificent concert grand piano that was accompanying her, gently faded but the beautiful music continued. It was Prozio Bernardo who was singing.

Bessy, enchanted by the music, crept quietly downstairs to listen. There was Prozio Bernardo in the kitchen, preparing a special breakfast for his young great-niece, all the while singing one of his favourite melodies.

As the final notes drifted out of the kitchen window, Bessy applauded so enthusiastically that she gave her great uncle a fright!

"Mamma mia!" exclaimed Prozio Bernardo. "I didn't see you there bambina!"

"Sorry Prozio Bernardo, I didn't mean to make you jump! That was so beautiful," said Bessy.

Henri tooted in admiration from the garage and the little birds that visited the garden everyday had stopped eating their crumbs and chirped loudly on the windowsills.

"Please, will you teach me to sing like that?" begged Bessy.

"Of course I will help you but I can only teach you so much. Most of the work has to come from you and you must practise every day," said the wise double bass.

"I will, I will!" cried Bessy excitedly and hurriedly ate her hearty breakfast of eggs and arpeggios so she could begin her lesson with Prozio Bernardo straight away.

Over the next few days, Bessy worked hard and listened carefully to her great-uncle as he talked of scales and studies and explained various performance techniques.

The wise, grand old double bass went on to tell Bessy all about his career, with stories from his time at Teatro alla Scala and from when he was a soloist in some of the world's most famous concert halls.

All too soon, Bessy came to the end of her stay with Prozio Bernardo. He lovingly prepared a huge hamper of all Bessy's favourite Italian food for her to take on the next part of her journey.

"Thank you so much for such an amazing time," said Bessy as she gave her great-uncle a big hug.

"Thank you for coming to visit me. Come back and see me again soon and remember to practise every day as I want to hear a recital from you next time!"

Bessy giggled and promised to work hard.

Henri reversed out of the driveway and the happy travellers were on the road once more. Bessy was smiling brightly, feeling inspired by her wise great-uncle and was already planning what wonderful pieces she should prepare for her next visit.

Chapter 5 – And on to Germany

Bessy and Henri trundled along the picturesque roads, round sharp bends, up steep hills and down, through lush, green valleys. They sang songs, chatted and enjoyed the feast which Prozio Bernardo had made for them. After a long while, Bessy saw a sign which read "Berlin 50km."

"Not much further now!" she exclaimed.

"Yipee!" tooted Henri, who was beginning to feel the wear on his tyres. An hour later Henri was negotiating the busy city traffic and safely delivered his tired but excited passenger to Petra's house in the centre of Berlin.

Petra was a beautiful concert grand piano who had not only accompanied great singers and instrumentalists but had also performed many solo recitals and concertos herself. Petra had accompanied Prozio Bernardo when he had come to Berlin years before to give a recital.

"Guten Abend Bessy!" called Petra from the window three floors up.

"Guten Abend Petra!" replied Bessy who was waving excitedly up to the window. She climbed out onto the pavement and unloaded her luggage.

This was where Bessy and Henri had to say "Au revoir" to each other. Henri was going to stay with his friend Gunter, a bright blue rally car, for a few days before going to meet Violette in Leipzig. Violette was auditioning for a position in the symphony orchestra there and Henri was going to meet her to take her home.

"Thank you so much," said Bessy to Henri. "It has been a wonderful trip."

"De rien," replied Henri, then quickly translated, "You're welcome! It certainly has been great fun. I have really enjoyed meeting your friends and family and learning new songs. Let's make another trip soon."

"Oooh yes!" agreed Bessy. "That would be wonderful." Henri tooted his horn and drove off into the distance.

Bessy picked up her luggage and took the lift up to Petra's apartment.

"Bessy! Bessy! How wonderful to see you said Petra as she gave the little bass a huge hug.

"My, how you've grown!" she exclaimed. Bessy smiled as she looked around the great drawing room in awe.

After a huge piece of Petra's famous Schwarzwälder Kirschtorte (Black Forest Cake), washed down with home-made lemonade, Petra announced that she was taking Bessy to a concert in the great cathedral across the square.

Bessy was thrilled. She was going to hear a baroque chamber orchestra play. The instruments in the orchestra were extremely old. They had strings made of gut instead of metal and funny shaped bows!

Bessy sat in the candlelit cathedral, gazing at the group of ancient instruments, transfixed by the beautiful music written hundreds of years ago by the composers Johann Sebastian Bach and George Frederich Handel.

13

"That was amazing!" whispered Bessy to Petra as the concert came to an end.

"Ja!" nodded Petra in agreement. "Now, you must come and meet Bruno."

Bruno was the only double bass in the orchestra.

"Guten Abend Bessy," said the old double bass in his beautiful, dulcet tones.

"Guten Abend," replied Bessy politely. "That was a very beautiful concert."

"You are most kind," said Bruno. The elderly bass, delighted to meet such an enthusiastic young bass, spent a long time telling her stories about baroque times. Bessy listened eagerly, taking note of everything that Bruno said.

A while later Petra caught sight of the church clock and gasped, "Goodness me, it is getting late and this young bass has a long journey to make early tomorrow morning!"

"Well it certainly has been lovely meeting you Bessy," said Bruno. "I do hope we meet again. Auf wiedersehen!"

"Auf wiedersehen," replied Bessy. "And thank you for telling me all those wonderful stories."

Petra and Bessy crossed the short distance back over the square to Petra's apartment to have a light supper.

"It really has been a wonderful day. The perfect end to a fantastic trip" said Bessy when she had finished her meal. "Thank you Petra."

"You are most welcome," replied Petra smiling. "It is such a pleasure to see you. Now, you must sleep well in preparation for your adventure tomorrow. Gute nacht."

Chapter 6 – Homeward bound!

The following morning, after a healthy breakfast of her favourite arpeggios, Bessy headed to the airport, escorted by Petra. Bessy was excited, as she had never been on an aeroplane before.

The flight attendants looked after her well and ensured that she had a great journey. The time passed quickly on the flight and before she knew it, she was checking that her seatbelt was secure, ready for landing.

She left the plane, thanked the flight attendants for looking after her so well and rushed to collect her suitcase. As she came through the sliding doors into the airport foyer, she immediately caught sight of her three faithful friends, Bertie Bagpipes, Fiona Fiddle and Dudley Drum.

"Welcome home Bessy!" chorused the three friends.

"Hello everyone! It's really great to see you! I had a wonderful time but missed you all so much. I have lots of stories to tell you and some new songs we can sing together!"

"Excellent!" replied Bertie. "We missed you too but we're glad you have had such a great time."

14

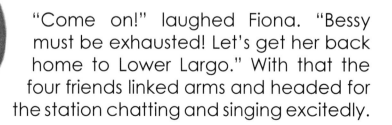

"Come on!" laughed Fiona. "Bessy must be exhausted! Let's get her back home to Lower Largo." With that the four friends linked arms and headed for the station chatting and singing excitedly.

"That was such a great trip," said Bessy to herself as she climbed the stairs yawning happily, with a steaming mug of hot milk in one hand and clutching a letter from her friend Suzy Saxophone from New York, in the other.

She took a sip of the milk and then opened the brightly coloured envelope.

"Dear Bessy," she read. "I hope this finds you well. I am writing to ask you if you will come over to New York to visit?"

Bessy had been bitten by the travel bug …

Next stop, New York!

Design Your OWN Musical Character
(And give it a name!)